Hermione Granger

Seamus Finnigan

Zacharis Smith

George Weasley

Fred Weasley

Alice Tolipan

Dumbledore Army

Ron Weasley

Neville Longbottom

Susan Bones

Hannah Abbott

Hermione Granger

Seamus Finnigan

Luca Caruso

Zacharias Smith

George Weasley

Fred Weasley

Ron Weasley

Katie Bell

Padma Patil

Parvati Patil

Cho Chang

Marietta Edgecombe

Neville Longbottom

Ginny Weasley

Luna Lovegood

Harry Potter

Ernie Macmillan

Hannah Abbott

Susan Bones

BBC Children's Books
The Penguin Group
80 Strand, London, WC2R 0RL
BBC Children's Books is an imprint of Children's Character Books, Ltd.
Illustration, text and design © Warner Bros Entertainment Inc. 2007
BBCB 6131
www.harrypotter.com
Printed in China

ISBN 9781405903356

Dumbledore's Army

Dumbledore's Army

Harry Potter
George Weasley
Fred Weasley
Ginny Weasley
Ron Weasley
Neville Longbottom
Padma Patil
Parvati Patil
Cho Chang
Zacharias Smith
Seamus Finnigan
Alice Tolipan
Luca Caruso
Marietta Edgecombe
Katie Bell
Hannah Abbott
Susan Bones

D.A.

D.A.

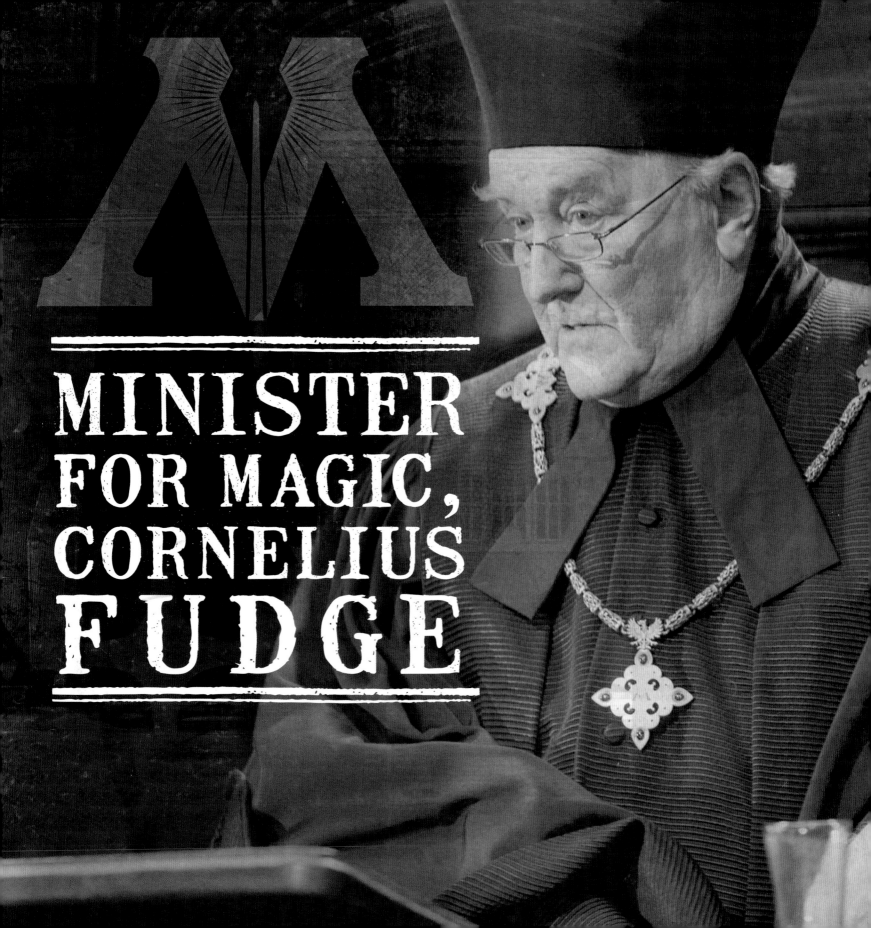

MINISTER
FOR MAGIC,
CORNELIUS
FUDGE

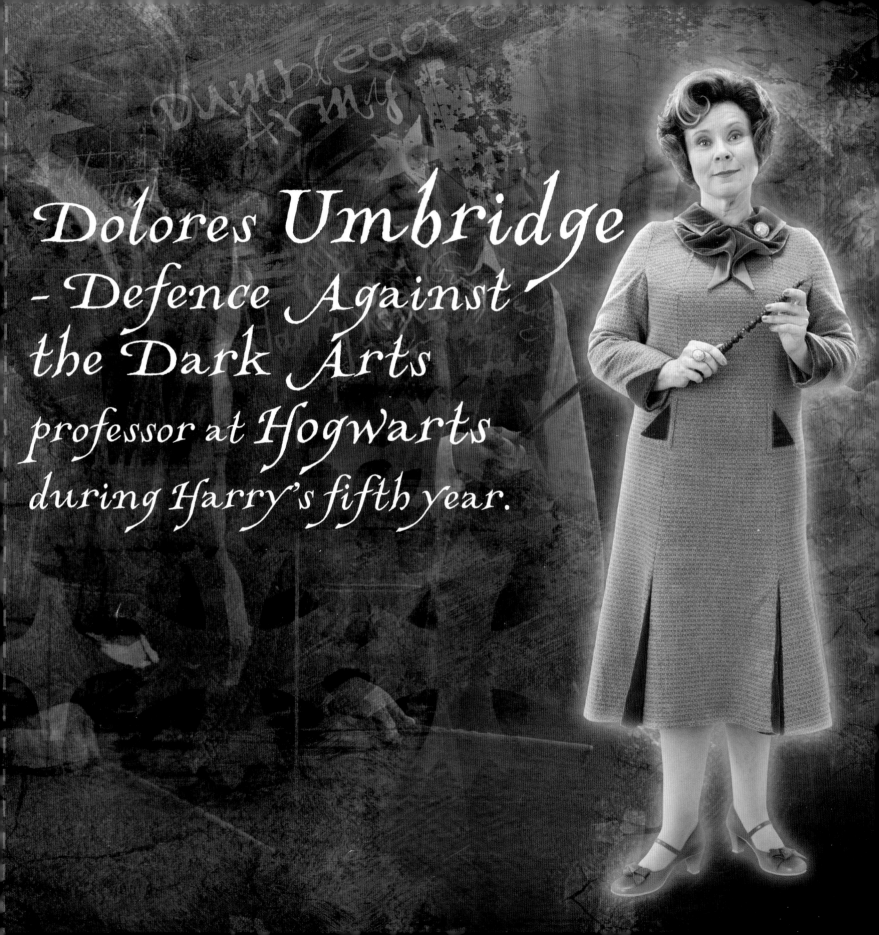

Dolores Umbridge

– Defence Against the Dark Arts professor at Hogwarts during Harry's fifth year.

Fred Weasley
Year 7
Gryffindor

Cho Chang
Year 6
Ravenclaw

Zacharias Smith
Year 5
Hufflepuff

Padma Patil
Year 5
Ravenclaw

Michael Corner
Year 5
Ravenclaw

Ginny Weasley
Year 4
Gryffindor

Parvati Patil
Year 5
Gryffindor

Dumbledore's Army

HARRY POTTER

THE BOY WHO LIVED

In his fifth
year, Harry
is chosen to lead
Dumbledore's
Army.

Hogwarts House:
Gryffindor

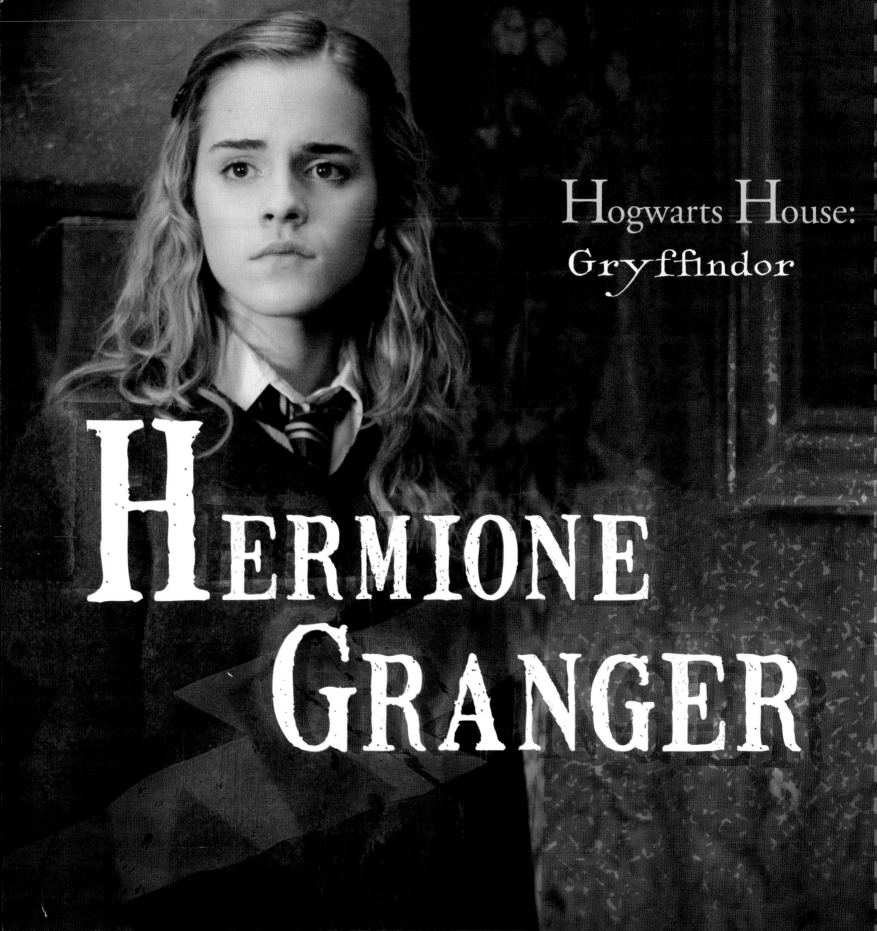

Hogwarts House:
Gryffindor

HERMIONE GRANGER

Hogwarts House:
Gryffindor

WEASLEY

LUNA LOVEGOOD

Hogwarts House:
Ravenclaw

CHO CHANG

Hogwarts House:
Ravenclaw

NEVILLE LONGBOTTOM

Hogwarts House:
Gryffindor

GINNY WEASLEY

Hogwarts House:
Gryffindor

THE FIGHT SO FAR: YEAR

FOR HARRY, THE STRUGGLE AGAINST VOLDEMORT BEGAN LONG BEFORE THE D.A. WAS FOUNDED.

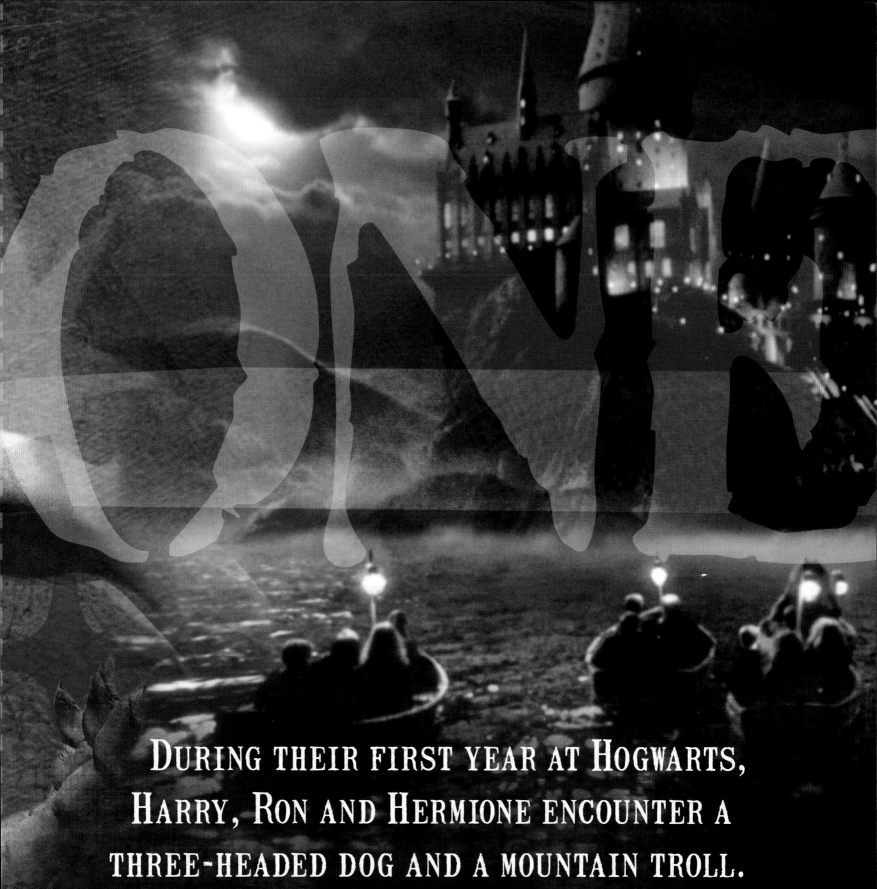

DURING THEIR FIRST YEAR AT HOGWARTS,
HARRY, RON AND HERMIONE ENCOUNTER A
THREE-HEADED DOG AND A MOUNTAIN TROLL.

THE FIGHT SO FAR: YEAR ONE

THE POTIONS MASTER

Since Harry's first year at Hogwarts, he has

suspected Severus Snape, the Potions Master,

of being associated with Lord Voldemort.

THE PHILOSOPHER'S STONE

The Stone will transform any

metal into pure gold, and produces

the Elixir of Life, which will make

the drinker immortal.

THE INVISIBILITY CLOAK

During his first Christmas

at Hogwarts, Harry receives his

father's Invisibility Cloak.

FRIGHT IN THE FOREST

IN THE FORBIDDEN FOREST, HARRY ENCOUNTERS THE BODY OF A UNICORN BEING DRAINED OF BLOOD BY A DARK, HOODED FIGURE.

THE MIRROR OF ERISED

*T*he Mirror of Erised

proves an unexpected ally

to Harry as he tries to keep

Voldemort from getting the

Philosopher's Stone.

THE FIGHT SO FAR: YEAR

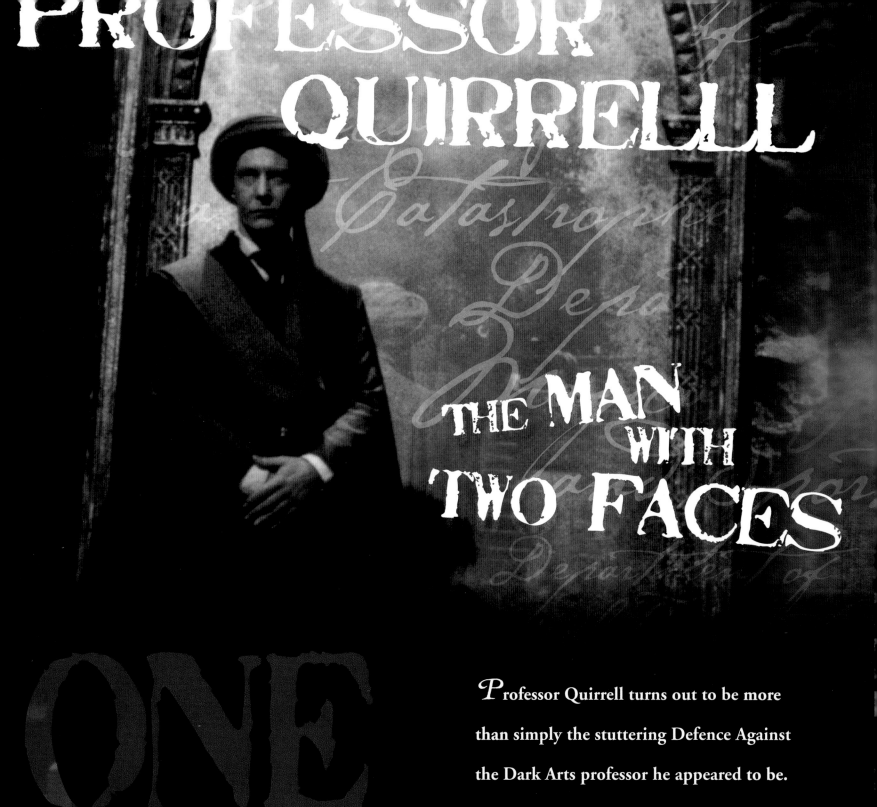

PROFESSOR QUIRRELL

THE MAN WITH TWO FACES

ONE

Professor Quirrell turns out to be more than simply the stuttering Defence Against the Dark Arts professor he appeared to be.

THE FIGHT SO FAR: YEAR TWO

DOBBY'S WARNING

A house-elf named Dobby warns
Harry not to return to Hogwarts.

THE CHAMBER OF SECRETS

*C*reated by Salazar Slytherin, the Chamber

is rumoured to contain a terrible monster.

THE HEIR OF SLYTHERIN

Some Hogwarts students suspect Harry is the
heir of Slytherin because he is a Parselmouth.

TOM RIDDLE'S DIARY

*I*n the girl's bathroom, Harry and Ron find an empty diary, with the name 'T.M. Riddle' on it.

THE FIGHT SO FAR: YEAR TWO

Friends in trouble

*H*ermione is Petrified by the monster

from the Chamber of Secrets.

Aragog

*H*arry and Ron follow a trail
of spiders that leads them to
Aragog, a giant spider.

Harry's second year at Hogwarts.

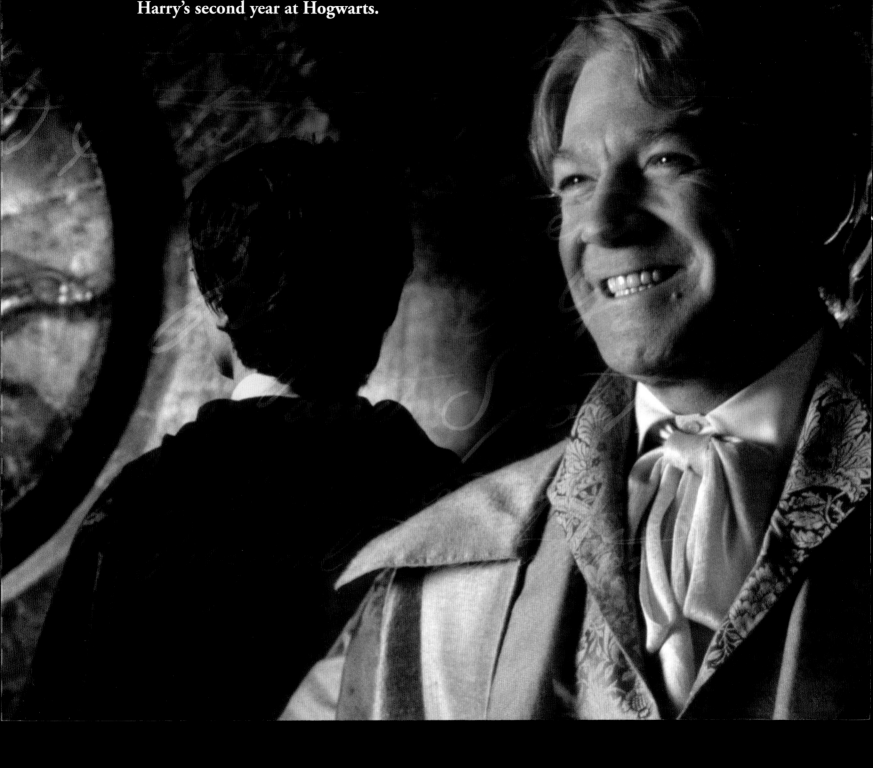

THE FIGHT SO FAR: YEAR TWO

*H*arry encounters Tom Riddle in the Chamber, and

learns that he is really Lord Voldemort.

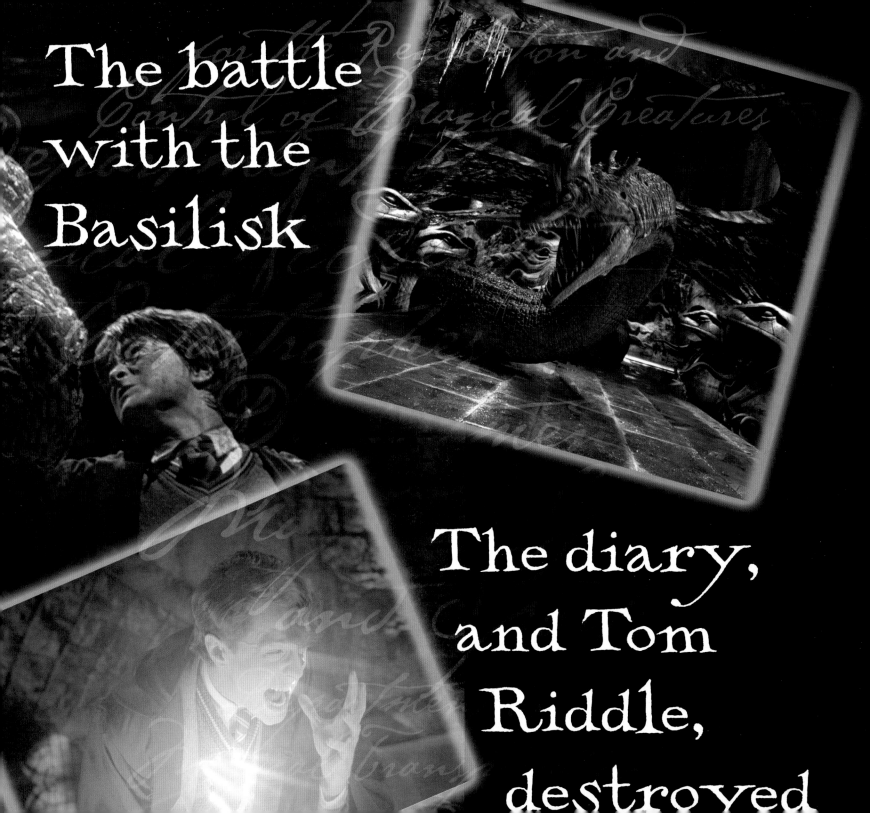

The battle with the Basilisk

The diary, and Tom Riddle, destroyed

THE FIGHT SO FAR: YEAR THREE

HARRY'S THIRD YEAR
AT HOGWARTS BEGINS
AMID WIDESPREAD PANIC:
CONVICTED MURDERER
SIRIUS BLACK HAS BROKEN
OUT OF THE WIZARD PRISON,
AZKABAN

HAVE YOU SEEN THIS WIZARD?

AZKABAN PRISON

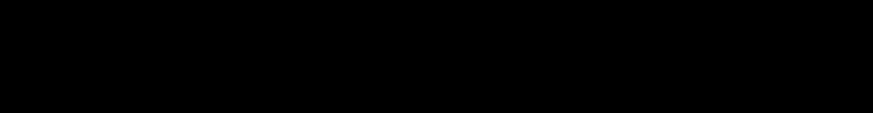

THE FIGHT SO FAR: YEAR THREE

*H*arry and Hermione use the Time-Turner to rescue Buckbeak from execution.

Ron in trouble

*H*arry and Hermione watch as Ron is dragged

into the base of the Whomping Willow by a large,

black dog.

THE FIGHT
SO FAR:
YEAR
THREE

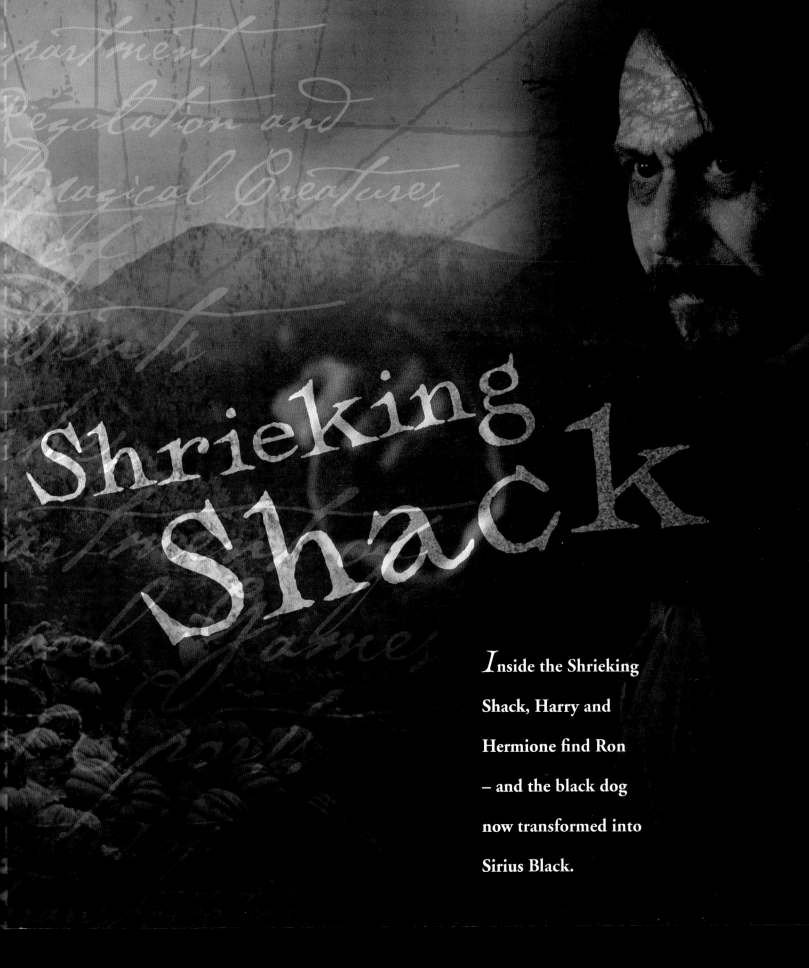

Shrieking Shack

*I*nside the Shrieking Shack, Harry and Hermione find Ron – and the black dog now transformed into Sirius Black.

THE FIGHT SO FAR: YEAR THREE

Transformation

*I*n the confusion caused by Professor Lupin's tranformation into a werewolf, Peter Pettigrew returned to his Animagus form – a rat – and escaped.

TRIWIZARD CHAMPIONS

FLEUR DELACOUR

THE FIGHT SO FAR?

CEDRIC DIGGORY

VIKTOR KRUM

YEAR FOUR

The First Task

THE FIGHT SO FAR: YEAR FOUR

The Golden Egg

The Third Task

THE FIGHT SO FAR: YEAR FOUR

THE GRAVEYARD

THE DUEL

THE FIGHT SO FAR: YEAR FOUR

*H*arry arrives back at Hogwarts, clutching Cedric's body.

BARTY CROUCH JR.

YEAR FIVE

HARRY AND DUDLEY ARE
ATTACKED BY DEMENTORS
IN LITTLE WHINGING.

THE
ADVANCE
GUARD

·ORDER·
OF THE PHOENIX

A secret society founded by Dumbledore to fight the Dark Lord during his first rise to power.

NYMPHADORA TONKS

'TONKS'

A Metamorphagus – she is able to change her appearance at will.

ALBUS
DUMBLEDORE

Headmaster of
Hogwarts School
of Witchcraft
and Wizardry

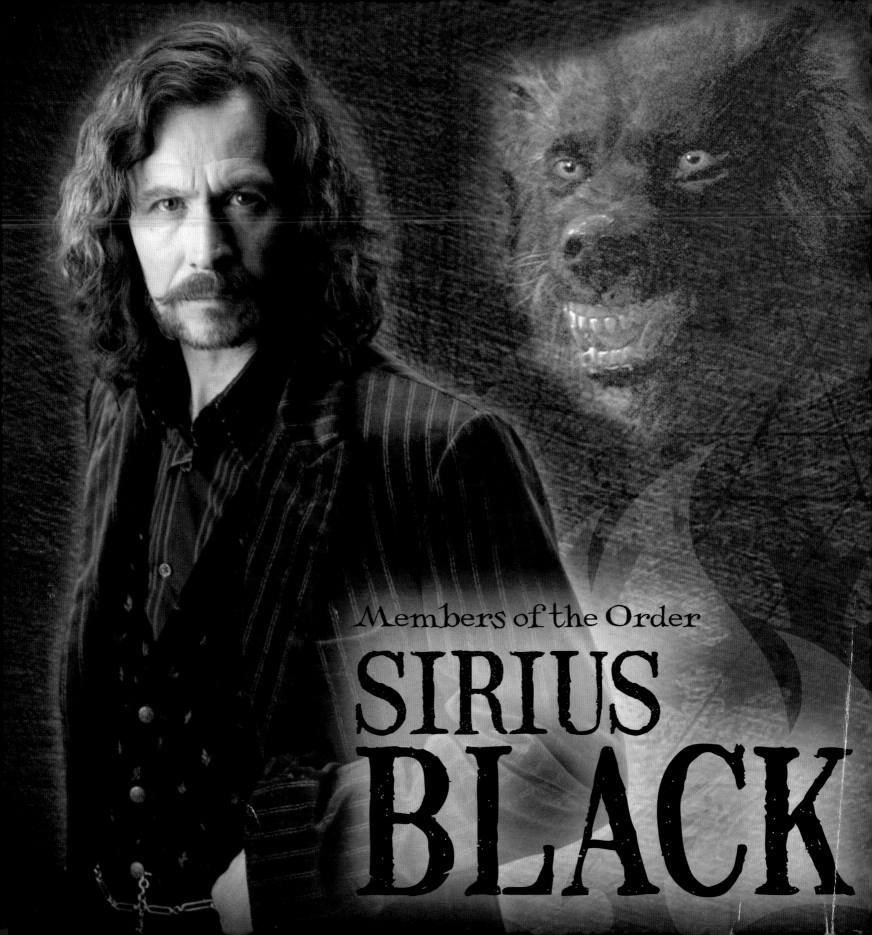

Members of the Order

SIRIUS BLACK

Harry's godfather.

An Animagus — he is able to turn into a large black dog.

ORDER
OF THE PHOENIX
HEADQUARTERS

Number twelve,
Grimmauld Place
belonged to the Black
family, and is now
owned by Sirius Black.

Members of the Order

RUBEUS HAGRID

Keeper of the Keys and Grounds at Hogwarts
School of Witchcraft and Wizardry

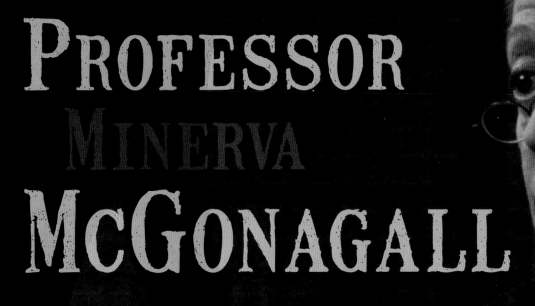

PROFESSOR MINERVA McGONAGALL

Deputy Headmistress
of Hogwarts School of
Witchcraft and Wizardry

REMUS LUPIN
('MOONY')

Defence Against the Dark Arts teacher at Hogwarts during Harry's third year

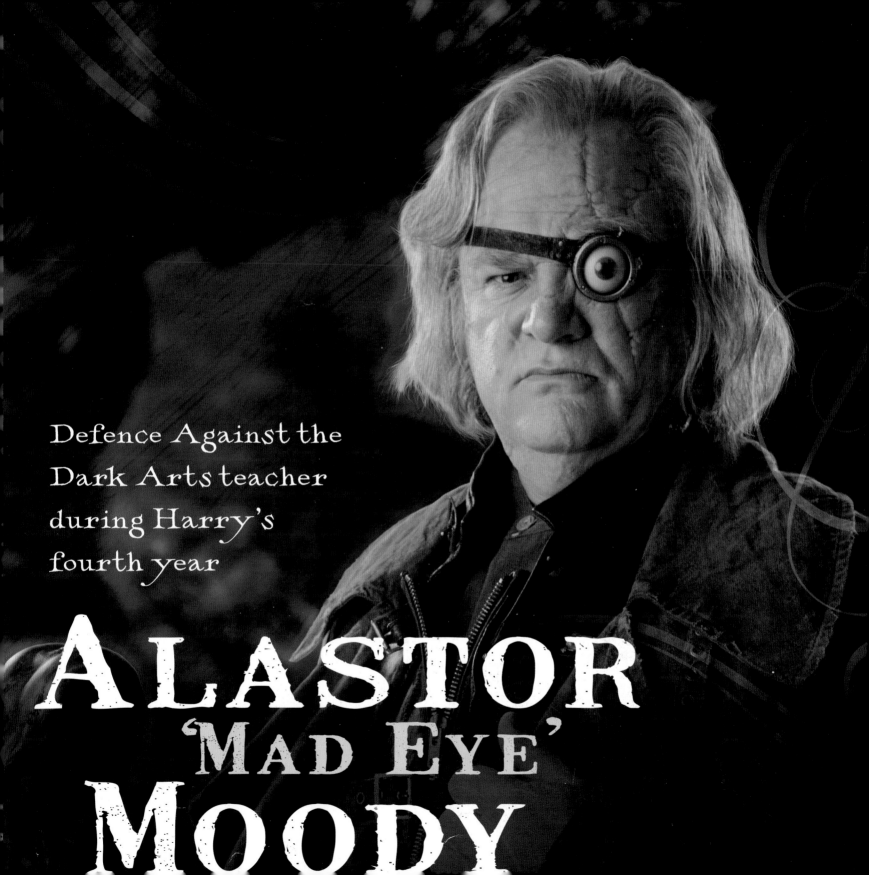

Defence Against the
Dark Arts teacher
during Harry's
fourth year

ALASTOR
'MAD EYE'
MOODY

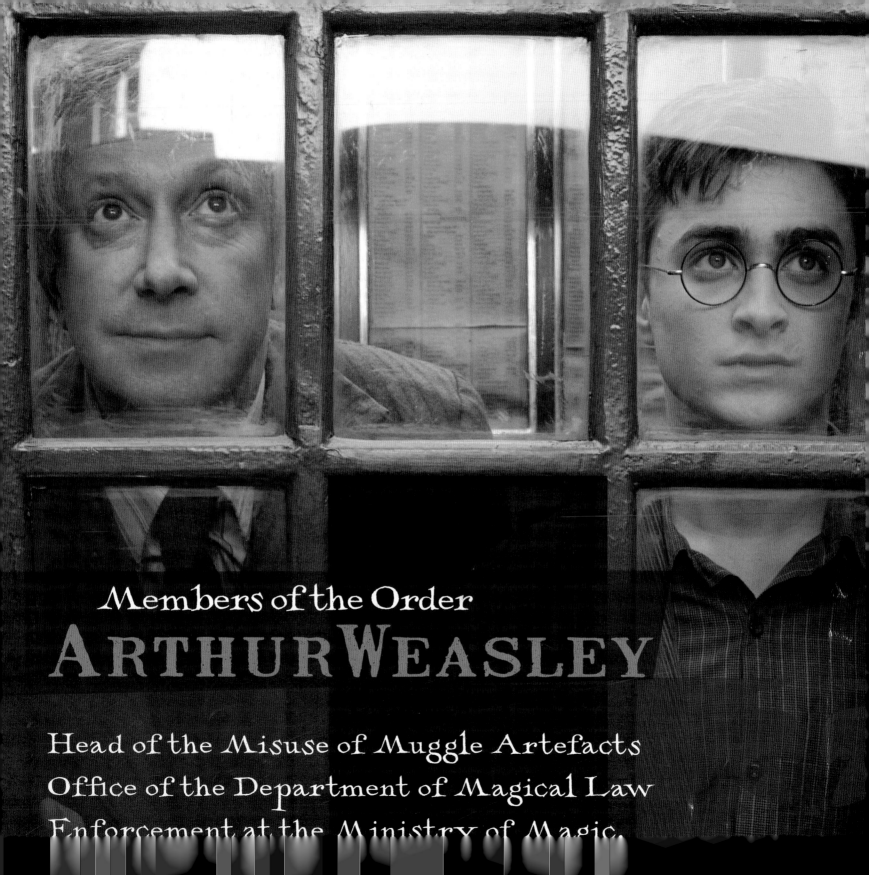

Members of the Order
ARTHUR WEASLEY

Head of the Misuse of Muggle Artefacts
Office of the Department of Magical Law
Enforcement at the Ministry of Magic.

MOLLY WEASLEY

The mother of the seven Weasley children, including Ron.

Members of the Order

PROFESSOR
SEVERUS

SNAPE

Potions Master
at Hogwarts
during Harry's
first five years

THE SECOND WAR: YEAR FIVE

THE HEARING

*H*arry is summoned to a hearing at the Ministry for using magic in the presence of a Muggle.

OCCLUMENCY

*D*umbledore asks Snape to teach Harry

Occlumency – the magical defence of the mind

against external penetration.

Voldemort

Lord Voldemort

He-Who-Must-Not-Be-Named

DEATH
EATERS —

the followers
of **Lord Voldemort.**

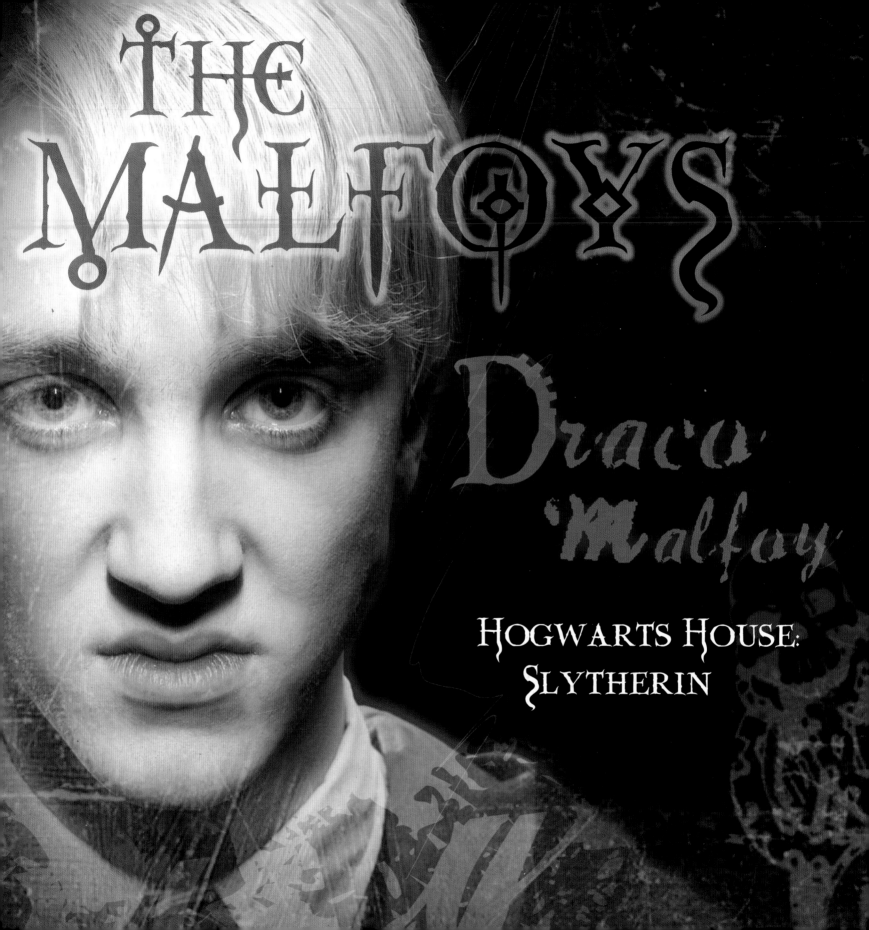

THE MALFOYS

Draco Malfoy

Hogwarts House: Slytherin

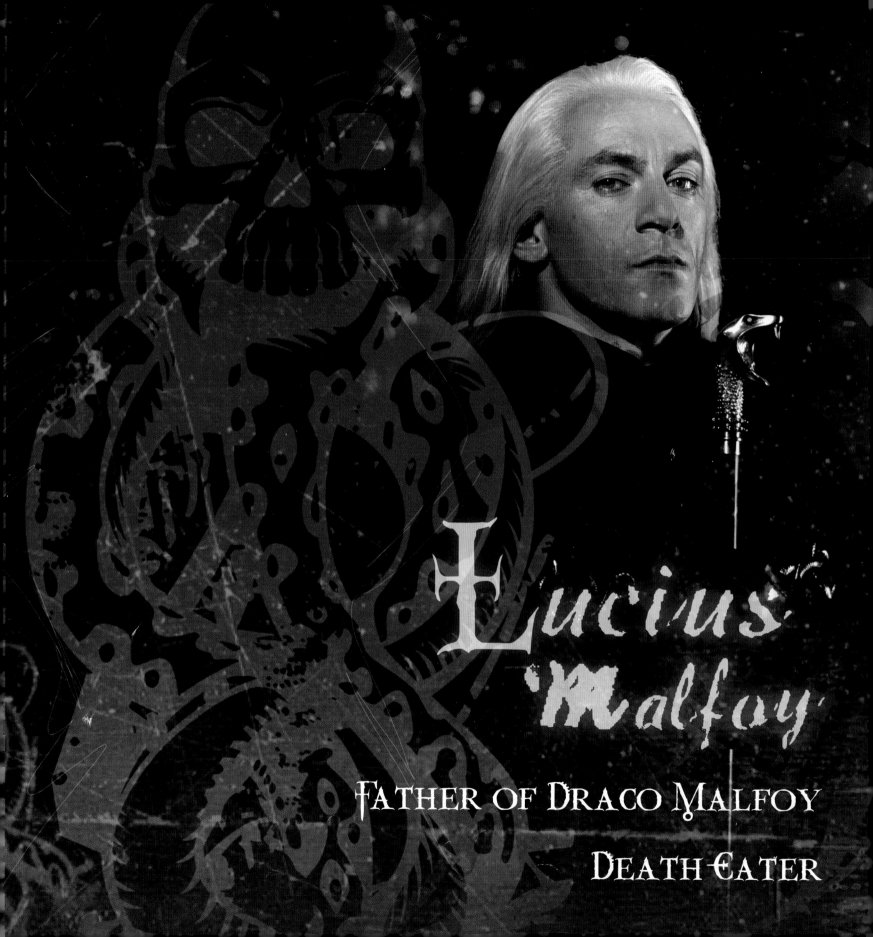

Lucius Malfoy

Father of Draco Malfoy

Death Eater

peter pettigrew

('WORMTAIL')

Bellatrix Lestrange

Death Eater

Cousin of Sirius Black

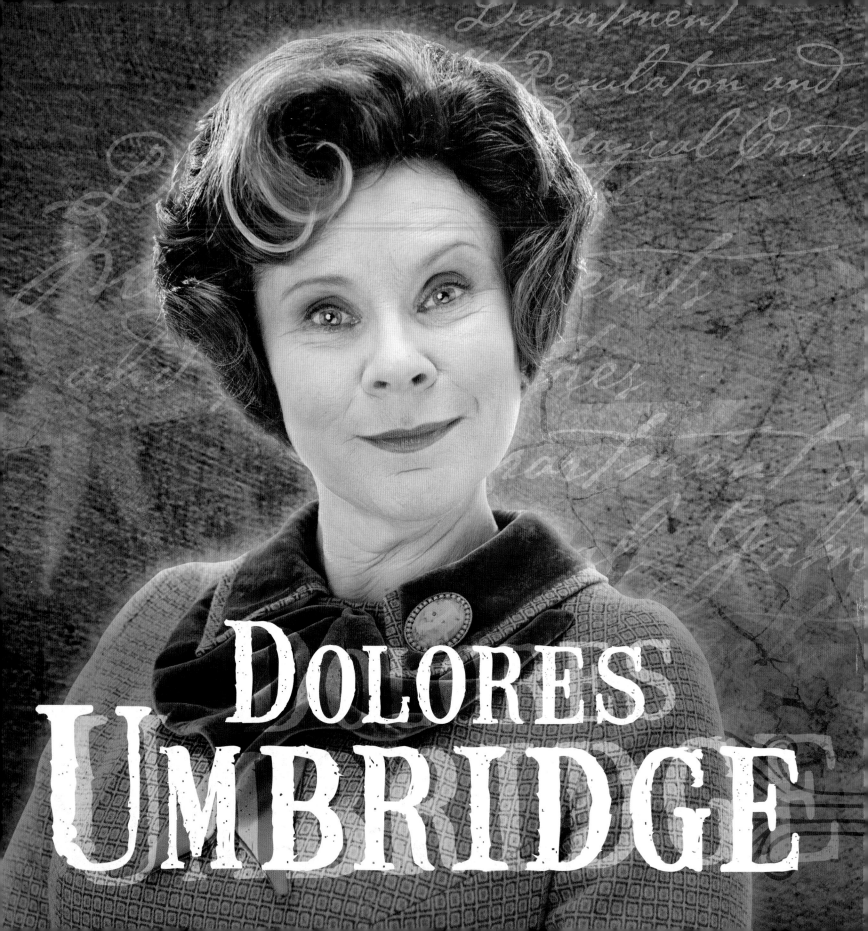

Dolores Umbridge

APPOINTED
HOGWARTS 👈 HIGH
INQUISITOR

BY MINISTER FOR MAGIC,
CORNELIUS FUDGE.

THE ROOM OF REQUIREMENT

First Kiss

Expecto Patronum

The Patronus Charm – used to conjure a
Patronus to repel Dementors.

Stupefy

The Stunning Spell

Impedimenta
Used to stop or slow down a person or object.

Training

Expelliarmus
The Disarming Spell Charm

THE SECOND WAR: YEAR FIVE

The D.A. discovered

High Inquisitor to Headmistress

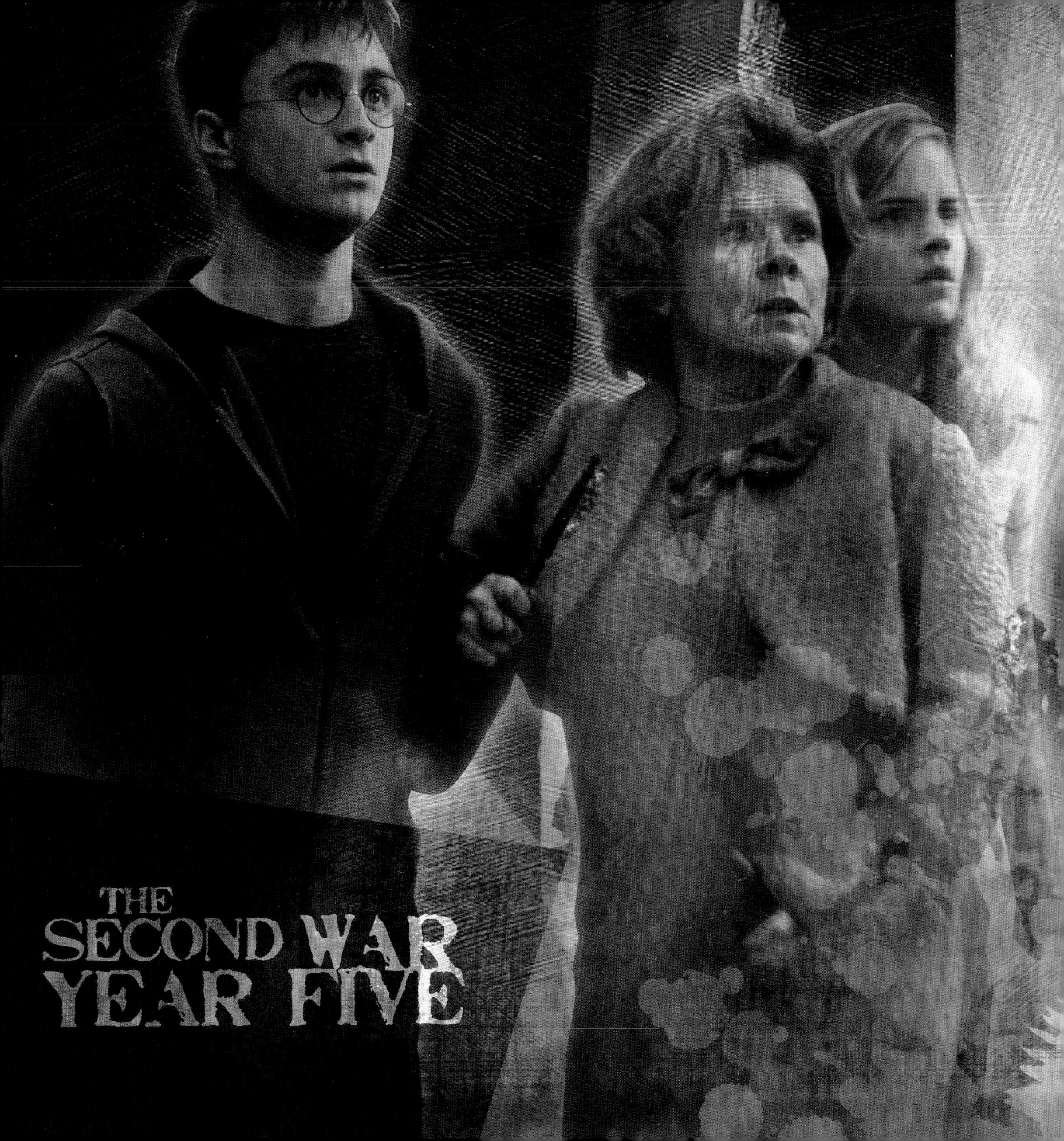

THE SECOND WAR YEAR FIVE

CENTAURS

GRAWP

GRAWP

HAGRID'S GIANT HALF-BROTHER

HARRY AND OTHER D.A. MEMBERS USE THESTRALS TO GET TO THE MINISTRY OF MAGIC TO RESCUE SIRIUS.

THE D.A.'S FIRST BATTLE

Harry and the other D.A. members walk straight into a trap set by Voldemort and his Death Eaters.

DUMBLEDORE
EVENTUALLY
ARRIVES
AND BATTLES
VOLDEMORT.

THE SECOND WAR HAS BEGUN

DUMBLEDORE TELLS HARRY ABOUT THE PROPHECY AND WHAT IT MEANS — THAT NEITHER HARRY NOR VOLDEMORT CAN LIVE WHILE THE OTHER SURVIVES.

Hermione Granger

Seamus Finnigan

Luca Caruso

George Weasley

Zacharias Smith

Hermione

Fred Weasley

Ron Weasley

Katie Bell

Padma Patil

Parvati Patil

Cho Chang

Marietta Edgecombe

Neville Longbottom

Luna Lovegood

Ginny Weasley

Ernie Macmillan

Harry Potter

Hannah Abbott

Susan Bones

Hermione Granger

Seamus Finnigan

Luca Caruso

Zacharias Smith

George Weasley

Fred Weasley

Ron Weasley

Katie Bell

Padma Patil

Parvati Patil

Cho Chang

Marietta Edgecombe

Neville Longbottom

Luna Lovegood

Ginny Weasley

Harry Potter

Ernie Macmillan

Hannah Abbott

Susan Bones